IMAGINE THAT™

Licensed exclusively to Imagine That Publishing Ltd
Tide Mill Way, Woodbridge, Suffolk, IP12 1AP, UK
www.imaginethat.com
Copyright © 2019 Imagine That Group Ltd
All rights reserved
4 6 8 9 7 5 3
Manufactured in China

Written by Pip Williams
Illustrated by Richard Watson

ISBN 978-1-78958-304-5

A catalogue record for this book is available from the British Library

One Little Dinosaur

Pip Williams
Richard Watson

One little dinosaur counts ten dotty rocks.

Two smart dinosaurs
wear nine snazzy socks.

Three hungry dinosaurs
eat eight yummy cakes.

Four scared dinosaurs run
from seven hissing snakes.

Five curious dinosaurs follow six leaping frogs.

Six happy dinosaurs play with five noisy dogs.

Seven brave dinosaurs climb four rocky trails.

Eight stripy dinosaurs with three spots on their tails.

Nine dinosaurs roar and
two dinosaurs wave.

Ten snoring dinosaurs
sleep in one big cave.

Dinosaurs can count
from one to ten ...

And count from ten to one again!